KAROLIINA KORHONEN

# FINNISH NIGHTMARES

A DIFFERENT KIND OF SOCIAL GUIDE TO FINLAND

ATENA

13th EDITION

© KAROLIINA KORHONEN

HTTP://FINNISHNIGHTMARES.BLOGSPOT.FI

PROOFREADING: HANNA MOY

WWW.ATENA.FI

ISBN 978-952-300-222-7

OTAVAN KIRJAPAINO OY, KEURUU 2018

MEET MATTI, A STEREOTYPICAL FINN WHO
APPRECIATES PEACE, QUIET AND PERSONAL SPACE.

MATTI TRIES HIS BEST TO DO UNTO OTHERS AS
HE WISHES TO BE DONE UNTO HIM: TO GIVE SPACE,
BE POLITE AND NOT BOTHER WITH UNNECESSARY
CHIT CHAT. AS YOU MIGHT'VE GUESSED, IT CAN'T
ALWAYS GO THAT WAY.

IF YOU FEEL UNCOMFORTABLE WHEN READING THESE
COMICS, YOU JUST MIGHT HAVE A TINY MATTI
LIVING IN YOU.

# FINNISH NIGHTMARES

—

## BEING A FINN

WHEN SOMEONE TAKES FINNISH STEREOTYPES TOO SERIOUSLY.

WHEN FOR SOME REASON, SOMEONE SOMEWHERE DOESN'T LIKE FINLAND.

WHEN SOMEONE THROWS WATER
ON THE SAUNA STOVE WITHOUT ASKING FIRST.

# FINNISH FACTS

EVEN THE MOST RESERVED FINN
CAN BECOME CHATTY IN A SAUNA.

# FINNISH NIGHTMARES

---

# NEIGHBORS

WHEN YOU WANT TO LEAVE YOUR APARTMENT
BUT YOUR NEIGHBOR IS IN THE HALLWAY.

WHEN YOU MEET YOUR NEIGHBOR MORE THAN ONCE
WITHIN A SHORT TIME.

SHARING AN ELEVATOR WITH A STRANGER.

WHEN YOUR NEIGHBOR IS NOISY AFTER 10PM.

WHEN YOU GET CAUGHT WHILE LEAVING A HEIPPALAPPU.*

*AN ANONYMOUS NOTE THAT'S LEFT IN AN APARTMENT HALLWAY FOR THE NEIGHBORS

WHEN RANDOM CHILDREN THINK YOU HAVE PREPARED FOR TRICK-OR-TREATING.
(IT'S REALLY NOT A THING IN FINLAND.)

# FINNISH NIGHTMARES

—

# PUBLIC PLACES

WHEN PUBLIC TRANSPORT IS LATE.

WHEN SOMEONE INVADES YOUR PERSONAL SPACE
WHILE YOU'RE WAITING FOR THE BUS.

WHEN THE WEATHER IS HORRIBLE, BUT THE ONLY SHELTER IS OCCUPIED.

WHEN YOU RUN TO CATCH A BUS

AND HAVE TO TRY AND ACT
LIKE YOU'RE NOT OUT OF BREATH.

WHEN YOU FLAG DOWN
THE WRONG BUS

AND YOU FEEL LIKE YOU HAVE
NO CHOICE BUT TO GET ON.

WHEN THE BUS IS "FULL".

WHAT NICE WEATHER!

WHEN SOMEONE SITS NEXT TO YOU ON PUBLIC TRANSPORT

AND THEN THEY START SPEAKING TO YOU.

WHEN SOMEONE NEXT TO YOU
MOVES TO A VACANT SEAT

AND YOU START TO WONDER
WHAT'S WRONG WITH YOU.

WHEN YOU SEE A SEAT BECOME VACANT, BUT DON'T WANT THE PERSON
NEXT TO YOU TO THINK YOU'RE MOVING BECAUSE OF THEM.

WHEN YOU WANT TO GET OFF THE BUS WITHOUT
BOTHERING THE PERSON SITTING NEXT TO YOU.

WHEN THE STOP BUTTON IN THE
PUBLIC TRANSPORT DOESN'T WORK

AND YOU HAVE TO YELL TO
THE DRIVER TO STOP.

WHEN IT'S CROWDED AND YOU DON'T WANT TO BOTHER ANYONE.

WHEN SOMEONE IS TALKING LOUDLY IN PUBLIC.

WHEN YOU GET IN A MOVIE THEATRE AT THE LAST MINUTE
AND YOUR SEAT IS IN THE MIDDLE.

WHEN YOU SLIP AND SOMEONE SEES

ARE YOU HURT?
SHOULD I CALL AN AMBULANCE?

NO. I'M PERFECTLY FINE.

AND IT GETS EVEN WORSE WHEN
THEY COME TO ASK IF YOU'RE HURT.

# FINNISH NIGHTMARES

——

# SHOPPING

WHEN A SALESPERSON ASKS YOU IF YOU NEED HELP.

WHEN YOU'VE TOLD A SALESPERSON THAT
YOU DON'T NEED HELP, BUT ACTUALLY YOU DO.

WHEN YOU WANT TO TAKE A FREE SAMPLE
BUT YOU DON'T WANT TO CHAT WITH THE SALESPERSON.

WHEN A SALESPERSON ACCIDENTALLY TOUCHES YOU.

WHEN THE SELF-SERVICE CHECKOUT DOESN'T WORK.

WHEN YOU FORGET TO BUY SOMETHING AND
HAVE TO GO BACK TO THE SAME SHOP.

# FINNISH NIGHTMARES

—

## FOOD & DINING

WHEN THERE'S NO COFFEE.

WHEN YOU CAN'T HAVE MILK TO DRINK WITH DINNER.

WHEN YOU CLEAN YOUR PLATE
AND YOUR HOST THINKS YOU'RE STILL HUNGRY.

WHEN YOU ANSWER YES TO AN EITHER/OR QUESTION AND
ARE TOO EMBARRASSED TO CORRECT THEM IF THEY ASSUME WRONG.

WHEN YOU GET
BAD CUSTOMER SERVICE

AND YOU START TO WONDER
WHAT <u>YOU</u> DID WRONG.

WHEN YOU'RE REALLY HUNGRY
BUT NOBODY WANTS TO BE THE FIRST TO TAKE FOOD.

WHEN NOBODY DARES TO TAKE THE LAST PIECE OF CAKE
BUT EVERYONE WANTS IT.

WHEN THERE IS NO ALMOND IN THE RICE PORRIDGE.

WHEN SOMEONE THINKS YOU'RE PRANKING THEM WITH MÄMMI.

# FINNISH NIGHTMARES

---

## SOCIAL RELATIONS

WHEN A STRANGER LOOKS
YOU IN THE EYES

AND SMILES.

WHEN YOU SEE SOMEONE YOU KNOW BUT AREN'T SURE
IF YOU KNOW THEM WELL ENOUGH TO GREET THEM.

WHEN SOMEONE YOU DON'T KNOW VERY WELL
TRIES TO GREET YOU BY KISSING OR HUGGING.

# FINNISH FACTS

HI MATTI.

HI.

HOW ARE YOU DOING?

VERY GOOD.

I'M NOT TOO BAD EITHER.
THE WEATHER IS GREAT ISN'T IT?

YES.

I WISH IT WAS LIKE THIS MORE FREQUENTLY.

AHA.

SO WHERE ARE YOU GOING NOW?

TO THE CITYMARKET.

GOING TO DO A LITTLE SHOPPING?

YEAH.

WHAT ARE YOU GOING TO BUY?

FOOD.

THAT'S GREAT.
WELL, YOU BETTER GET GOING. BYE.

## "SMALL" TALK

ANSWERING SERIOUSLY TO SMALL TALK.

WHEN SOMEONE REPEATS YOUR NAME.

WHEN AN ACQUAINTANCE STANDS
TOO CLOSE WHEN TALKING TO YOU

AND THEN THEY CASUALLY
TOUCH YOU.

WAITING PATIENTLY FOR YOUR TURN TO SPEAK.

HAVING TO PRAISE YOURSELF.

GIVING A SPEECH.

WHEN SOMEONE'S DOING SOMETHING 'WRONG'
AND STARING AT THEM INTENSELY WON'T MAKE THEM STOP.

# FINNISH NIGHTMARES

---

# AT WORK

BEING SICK BUT GOING TO WORK SO YOU DON'T SEEM LAZY.

WHEN A CO-WORKER WANTS TO CHAT AND
YOU HAVE TO PRETEND YOU'RE BUSY.

WHEN YOU ARRIVE LATE TO A MEETING AND
EVERYONE'S LOOKING AT YOU.

SO. DOES ANYONE
HAVE ANY QUESTIONS?

WHEN YOU <u>DO</u> HAVE A QUESTION,
BUT YOU DON'T WANT THE SPOTLIGHT.

WHEN YOU GET PAIRED WITH SOMEONE THAT YOU DON'T KNOW.

WHEN YOU FAIL TO EXPRESS YOUR EXCITEMENT.

GETTING PRAISED.

# FINNISH DAYDREAMS

GETTING SOMETHING FOR FREE
(EVEN IF IT IS JUST A BUCKET).

NO HEI,
MATTI!

BEING INVITED TO THE "LINNAN JUHLAT".

SILENCE.

EMPTY PUBLIC TRANSPORT.

# I'D LIKE TO THANK

MIKA, MY BELOVED HUSBAND WHO KEEPS MY FEET ON THE GROUND.
KHALID BUR, MY GUARDIAN ANGEL IN THE WILD WORLD OF BUSINESS.
JOEL WILLANS & JULIEN BOURRELLE WHO GAVE ME PIVOTAL ADVICE
WHEN THE COMIC WENT VIRAL.

EVERYONE WHO HAS HAD THE PATIENCE TO LISTEN TO ME PRATTLE AND
BABBLE ABOUT FINNISH NIGHTMARES.

AND MOST IMPORTANTLY I'D LIKE TO THANK ALL THOSE WONDERFUL
PEOPLE WHO HAVE SHARED, COMMENTED ON AND LIKED MY COMICS.

THERE WOULD BE NO MATTI WITHOUT YOU.

# FINNISH SMILE

RARE AND GENUINE